JOSEPH HAYDN

SYMPHONY No. 95
C minor/c-Moll/Ut mineur
Hob. I:95

Edited by/Herausgegeben von
Harry Newstone

Ernst Eulenburg Ltd
London · Mainz · Madrid · New York · Paris · Tokyo · Toronto · Zürich

CONTENTS/INHALT

Preface/Vorwort III

Editorial Notes/Revisionsbericht VI

Textual Notes XV

I. Allegro moderato 1

II. Andante cantabile 23

III. Menuet/Trio 33

IV. Finale. Vivace 40

© 1999 Ernst Eulenburg & Co GmbH, Mainz
for Europe excluding the British Isles
Ernst Eulenburg Ltd, London
for all other countries

All rights reserved.
No part of this publication may be reproduced, stored in a retrieval system,
or transmitted in any form or by any means,
electronic, mechanical, photocopying, recording or otherwise,
without the prior written permission of the publisher:

Ernst Eulenburg Ltd
48 Great Marlborough Street
London W1V 2BN

PREFACE/VORWORT

In the autumn of 1790 Prince Nikolaus Joseph Esterházy, Haydn's employer and patron, died and his son, Prince Paul Anton, succeeded him. Almost at once the great (but considerably expensive) musical establishment which had for nearly thirty years nurtured the composer, and is now chiefly remembered for the glory he brought to it, was dismantled. Although still nominally *Capellmeister*, with a yearly pension, Haydn was at last free to travel wherever he wished, something he had not been able to do before. He returned to Vienna relieved of the daily pressures of court duties, but his respite was not to last long. Johann Peter Salomon, the German-born violinist and London impresario, was visiting Cologne when he heard of the death of Prince Nikolaus and lost no time in getting to Vienna determined to procure Haydn for his forthcoming London season. It was not the first time he had invited Haydn to England; now the composer was free to accept, and he did. A contract was exchanged and the two left Vienna in the middle of December and arrived in Dover on New Year's Day 1791.

Haydn stayed in England for a year and a half and returned for a second visit of similar duration in 1794-5. The stimulus he received from the London musical scene, the reception he was accorded there and the high quality of the musicians placed at his disposal inspired him to some of his finest music. The twelve symphonies he wrote for Salomon (six for each visit) are the summation of his orchestral achievement and the ground upon which the music he composed after his return to Vienna – notably the last

Im Herbst 1790 starb Fürst Nikolaus Joseph Esterházy, Haydns Dienstherr und Gönner; Fürst Paul Anton, sein Sohn, wurde sein Nachfolger. Fast unmittelbar hierauf wurde das bedeutende, allerdings ziemlich kostspielige Musikleben am Hofe eingestellt, das Haydn nahezu dreißig Jahre lang ernährt hatte, und an das man sich heute hauptsächlich des Glanzes wegen erinnert, den es durch den Komponisten erhalten hatte. Obwohl er auch weiterhin den Kapellmeistertitel führen durfte und eine jährliche Pension erhielt, konnte Haydn im Gegensatz zu früher nun schließlich nach Belieben reisen. Er kehrte nach Wien zurück, entlastet vom täglichen Zwang des Dienstes am Hofe, jedoch sollte diese Ruhepause nicht von langer Dauer sein. Als der deutschstämmige Geiger und Londoner Impresario Johann Peter Salomon während eines Aufenthaltes in Köln vom Tod des Fürsten Nikolaus erfuhr, eilte er unverzüglich nach Wien, entschlossen, Haydn für die kommende Saison nach London zu verpflichten. Dies war nicht das erste Mal, daß er Haydn nach England eingeladen hatte; jetzt jedoch war der Komponist in der Lage zuzusagen, und er tat es auch. Ein Vertrag wurde ausgehandelt, und die beiden verließen Wien Mitte Dezember und erreichten Dover am Neujahrstag 1791.

Haydn blieb anderthalb Jahre lang in England und kehrte 1794/95 zu einem zweiten, etwa gleich langen Aufenthalt zurück. Die Anregungen, die er durch das Londoner Musikleben erhielt, die Aufnahme dort und die hohe Qualität der ihm zur Verfügung stehenden Musiker inspirierten ihn zu mehreren seiner bedeutendsten Werke. So bilden die zwölf Sinfonien für Salomon (sechs für jeden Aufenthalt) die Zusammenfassung seiner ganzen Kunst der Orchesterkomposition und die Grundlage

six masses, *The Creation* and *The Seasons* – was based.

The most popular of the London symphonies are among the most frequently played of Haydn's works, yet for very many years they were (and often still are) performed from texts that had, during the 19th century, become seriously corrupted from the originals. The first modern attempt to present a uniform set of scores based upon authentic sources came with Ernst Praetorius's edition for Eulenburg in the 1930s. For this he consulted the autograph scores of Nos. 98, 99, 101, 102, 103 and 104 but not those of Nos. 94, 95, 96 and 100 (No. 93 has disappeared and the whereabouts of No. 97 was then unknown). One can only speculate on why Praetorius was not able to examine the autograph of No. 94 which was in the then Preußische Staatsbibliothek in Berlin, where he had seen those of Nos. 98, 99, 101, 102 and 104, or Nos. 95 and 96 which were in the British Museum along with No. 103 of which he had received a photocopy. Clearly, detailed knowledge of the whereabouts of Haydn autographs was still very sketchy in the 1930s and Praetorius probably had no way of knowing what we, with the benefit of a further 50 years of Haydn research, can take for granted. Thus Praetorius's edition, while the best available at the time and certainly an important step in the right direction was, not surprisingly, uneven.

The phase of Haydn research that was to result in no less than a renaissance was now well begun. In 1939 the distinguished Danish scholar Jens Peter Larsen published

für die Werke, die er nach seiner Rückkehr nach Wien schrieb – vor allem die sechs letzten Messen sowie die *Schöpfung* und die *Jahreszeiten*.

Die bekanntesten der Londoner Sinfonien gehören zu den meistgespielten Werken Haydns, jedoch wurden sie viele Jahre lang (vielfach noch bis in die heutige Zeit) aus Notenmaterial aufgeführt, das im 19. Jahrhundert gegenüber dem Originaltext erheblich verfälscht worden war. Den ersten neueren Versuch, aufgrund der authentischen Quellen einen einheitlichen Satz Partituren herauszubringen, stellt die Ausgabe von Ernst Praetorius im Rahmen der Edition Eulenburg in den 1930er Jahren dar. Er zog die Partitur-Autographe von Nr. 98, 99, 101, 102, 103 und 104 heran, nicht aber diejenigen von Nr. 94, 95, 96 und 100 (das Autograph von Nr. 93 ist verschollen, und das von Nr. 97 war damals nicht nachweisbar). Man kann nur Vermutungen darüber anstellen, warum Praetorius nicht in der Lage war, das Autograph von Nr. 94 zu untersuchen, das in der damaligen Preußischen Staatsbibliothek in Berlin lag, wo er auch die Autographe von Nr. 98, 99, 101, 102 und 104 eingesehen hatte; Nr. 95 und 96 waren ihm im British Museum London zugänglich, zusammen mit dem Autograph von Nr. 103, das ihm als Fotokopie vorlag. Auf jeden Fall war die Kenntnis der Aufbewahrungsorte von Haydn-Autographen in den 1930er Jahren noch sehr lückenhaft, und Praetorius konnte damals wohl kaum wissen, was wir heute, nach weiteren 50 Jahren Haydn-Forschung, als erwiesen betrachten können. So war es nicht verwunderlich, daß die Ausgaben von Praetorius in sich unheitlich waren, auch wenn sie zu ihrer Zeit die besten verfügbaren waren und sicherlich einen Schritt in die richtige Richtung unternahmen.

Damit hatte eine Zeit intensiver Haydn-Forschung begonnen, die eine regelrechte Renaissance auslöste. 1939 veröffentlichte der bedeutende dänische Musikwissen-

Die Haydn-Überlieferung and two years later a facsimile print of *Drei Haydn-Kataloge*, revealing for the first time the immensity of the subject. The post-war years saw the formation in London of the Haydn Orchestra and in Boston of the Haydn Society (both 1949). In 1954, the founder of the Haydn Society, H. C. Robbins Landon, in an article 'The original versions of Haydn's first 'Salomon' symphonies',[1] drew our attention to the extent to which the standard performing editions of these works (mostly Breitkopf & Härtel and Peters) were in many cases 'flagrant falsifications of Haydn's own texts'. For a discussion on how these alterations came about the reader is referred to that article as well as to Landon's *The Symphonies of Joseph Haydn*,[2] and his *Haydn – Chronicle and Works*, Vol. 3 *Haydn in England*.[3]

Since the mid-1950s Henle Verlag, Munich, has issued a number of volumes of Haydn symphonies as part of a Complete Edition of his works for the Haydn Institute of Cologne. Universal Edition, Vienna, issued all the symphonies during the 1960s in an edition by H. C. Robbins Landon.

In 1959, the present writer, with material and advice from Professor Landon, revised and conducted all the London symphonies in a series of BBC broadcasts commemorating the 150th anniversary of the composer's death. The aim was to get as close as possible to Haydn's original intentions not only from the scholar's point of view but from the performer's too.

[1] *The Music Review*, Vol. 15/1, 1954
[2] London, 1955
[3] London, 1976

The texts were accordingly prepared from a number of manuscript sources of primary authenticity and one early printed edition of unusual interest and importance. These same sources, which are listed below with their credentials, have been re-examined for this new edition together with other more recent discoveries.

Editorial Notes

Location and description of sources

I. Autograph scores and authentic manuscript copies

We retain, for convenience, the generally accepted numerical order established by Eusebius von Mandyczewski for the Breitkopf & Härtel Collected Edition (begun in 1907 but never completed) although, in the case of the first set of London symphonies, this is not thought to be the order in which they were composed or first performed.

No. 93 Autograph:
Whereabouts unknown, possibly lost. Seen in a Brunswick bookshop in 1870 by the Haydn biographer, Carl Ferdinand Pohl, who noted the date 1791 on it in Haydn's hand.

Copies:
1. Copy made in London for Salomon, with corrections in other hands – possibly Haydn's and Salomon's. Acquired by the Royal Philharmonic Society in 1847 from William Ayrton who had inherited all of Salomon's music in 1815. Acquired by the British Library, London, January 1988.[4]

---

[4] see Arthur Searle, 'Haydn Manuscripts in the British Library', *Early Music*, 5/1982, also *Haydn Yearbook XIV*

Der Notentext wurde aufgrund einer Anzahl handschriftlicher Primärquellen und einer besonders interessanten und wichtigen Druckausgabe erarbeitet. Diese unten verzeichneten und beschriebenen Quellen wurden für die Neuausgabe unter Berücksichtigung anderer neuerer Forschungsergebnisse nochmals untersucht.

Revisionsbericht

Quellen-Fundorte und Quellenbeschreibung

I. Partiturautographe und autorisierte Abschriften

Der Einfachheit halber wird die allgemein übliche Zählung nach der Gesamtausgabe von Eusebius von Mandyczewski bei Breitkopf & Härtel (unvollständig, begonnen 1907) beibehalten, obwohl sie vermutlich für die erste Folge der Londoner Sinfonien weder der Reihenfolge der Entstehung noch der Uraufführungen entspricht.

Nr. 93 Autograph:
Verschollen, möglicherweise verloren. Zuletzt 1870 in einer Braunschweiger Buchhandlung durch den Haydn-Biographen Carl Ferdinand Pohl nachgewiesen, der die Datierung 1791 von Haydns Hand feststellte.

Abschriften:
1. Abschrift aus London, angefertigt für Salomon, mit Korrekturen in anderer Handschrift – vermutlich von Haydn und Salomon. 1847 erworben durch die Royal Philharmonic Society London von William Ayrton, der 1815 von Salomon dessen gesamten Bestand an Noten geerbt hatte. Seit Januar 1988 im Besitz der British Library London[4].

---

[4] vgl. Arthur Searle, „Haydn Manuscripts in the British Library", *Early Music*, 5/1982, und *Haydn Jahrbuch XIV*

VII

2. Copy made by Esterházy copyist (Elßler or another with similar handwriting). Esterházy Archives, National Széchényi Library, Budapest.	2. Abschrift eines Kopisten am Hofe Esterházy (Elßler, der Haydns Kopist war, oder jemand mit ähnlicher Handschrift): Esterházy-Archiv der Széchényi-Nationalbibliothek Budapest.
No. 94 Autograph: Movements I, III and IV in the Staatsbibliothek zu Berlin – Preußischer Kulturbesitz, Musikabteilung, lacking last page of Mov. I and the first two pages of the Minuet. The missing page of Mov. I and the whole of Mov. II (in its original version before Haydn added the 'surprise') in the Library of Congress, Washington, D.C. Copies: 1. Salomon's London copy; details as No. 93. 2. Esterházy copy; details as No. 93. Both with later version of Mov. II (i.e., with 'surprise').	Nr. 94 Autograph: Satz I, III und IV: Staatsbibliothek zu Berlin – Preußischer Kulturbesitz, Musikabteilung (ohne die letzte Seite von Satz I und die ersten beiden Seiten des Menuetts). Die fehlende Seite von Satz I und der vollständige Satz II (in seiner ursprünglichen Fassung vor der Hinzufügung des „Paukenschlags" durch Haydn) befinden sich in der Library of Congress Washington D.C. Abschriften: 1. Salomons Londoner Abschrift; wie Nr. 93 2. Abschrift Esterházy: wie Nr. 93 (beide mit der späteren Fassung von Satz II, d.h. mit dem „Paukenschlag")
No. 95 Autograph: Royal Philharmonic Society collection, British Library, London. Bound together with autograph of No. 96 and copy of No. 98. Copies: None found – see III below.	Nr. 95 Autograph: Royal Philharmonic Society Sammlung, British Library London (zusammengebunden mit dem Autograph von Nr. 96 und der Abschrift von Nr. 98) Abschriften: Nicht nachweisbar (vgl. unten Abschnitt III)
No. 96 Autograph: Royal Philharmonic Society collection, British Library, London. Bound together with autograph of No. 95 and copy of No. 98. Copies: None found – see III below.	Nr. 96 Autograph: Royal Philharmonic Society Sammlung, British Library London (zusammengebunden mit dem Autograph von Nr. 95 und der Abschrift von Nr. 98) Abschriften: Nicht nachweisbar (vgl. unten Abschnitt III)
No. 97 Autograph: Owned by Mrs Eva Alberman, London (formerly Stefan Zweig collection); acquired by the British	Nr. 97 Autograph: Im Mai 1986 aus dem Besitz von Frau Eva Alberman, London, erworben durch die British Library

Library, London, May 1986.
Copy:
Salomon's London copy; details as No. 93.

No. 98 Autograph:
Formerly in the Preußische Staatsbibliothek, Berlin (from the Schindler Beethoven collection). Four pages missing from Mov. IV. Now in the Jagellonian University Library, Cracow.
Copy:
Salomon's London copy; details as No. 93. Bound together with the autographs of Nos. 95 and 96.

No. 99 Autograph:
Formerly in the Preußische Staatsbibliothek, Berlin. Now in the Jagellonian University Library, Cracow. Photocopy in Hoboken Photogramm Archiv, Vienna.
Copies:
1. Salomon's London copy; details as No. 93.
2. Elßler copy, Esterházy Archives, National Széchényi Library, Budapest.

No. 100 Autograph:
Esterházy Archives, National Széchényi Library, Budapest, lacking Mov. II.
Copy:
Salomon's London copy; details as No. 93.

No. 101 Autograph:
Formerly in the Preußische Staatsbibliothek, Berlin. Now in the Jagellonian University Library, Cracow. Photocopy in Hoboken Photogramm Archiv, Vienna.
Copies:
1. Salomon's London copy; details as No. 93.
2. Elßler copy, Esterházy Archives, National Széchényi Library, Budapest.

London (vormals Sammlung Stefan Zweig).
Abschrift:
Salomons Londoner Abschrift; wie Nr. 93

Nr. 98 Autograph:
Vormals Preußische Staatsbibliothek Berlin (aus der Beethoven-Sammlung Schindlers). Von Satz IV fehlen vier Seiten. Heute im Besitz der Biblioteka Jagiellońska Krakau.

Abschrift:
Salomons Londoner Abschrift; wie Nr. 93 (zusammengebunden mit den Autographen von Nr. 95 und 96)

Nr. 99 Autograph:
Vormals Preußische Staatsbibliothek Berlin; heute im Besitz der Biblioteka Jagiellońska Krakau. Fotokopien im Photogramm-Archiv Hoboken, Wien
Abschriften:
1. Salomons Londoner Abschrift; wie Nr. 93
2. Abschrift Elßler: Esterházy-Archiv der Széchényi-Nationalbibliothek Budapest

Nr. 100 Autograph:
Esterházy-Archiv der Széchényi-Nationalbibliothek Budapest (ohne Satz II)
Abschrift:
Salomons Londoner Abschrift; wie Nr. 93

Nr. 101 Autograph:
Vormals Preußische Staatsbibliothek Berlin; heute im Besitz der Biblioteka Jagiellońska, Krakau. Fotokopien im Photogramm-Archiv Hoboken, Wien
Abschriften:
1. Salomons Londoner Abschrift; wie Nr. 93
2. Abschrift Elßler: Esterházy-Archiv der Széchényi-Nationalbibliothek Budapest

No. 102 Autograph:
Staatsbibliothek zu Berlin – Preußischer Kulturbesitz, Musikabteilung, Berlin.
Copy:
Salomon's London copy; details as No. 93.

No. 103 Autograph:
British Library, London: three pages of Minuet in another hand.
Copy:
Salomon's London copy; details as No. 93.

No. 104 Autograph:
Staatsbibliothek zu Berlin – Preußischer Kulturbesitz, Musikabteilung, Berlin.
Copy:
Salomon's London copy; details as No. 93.

It will be seen that, with the exception of No. 93 and the missing slow movement of No. 100, the autograph scores of the London symphonies have survived very nearly intact. The copies made for Salomon in London are a recent (1982) discovery by Alec Hyatt King, and are of great importance.

II. Manuscript orchestral material by Johann Elßler

Orchestral parts copied from the autograph scores by Haydn's own copyist, many with corrections in the composer's hand, are obviously of great value in the establishment of accurate texts of the London symphonies. The most comprehensive collection of the London symphonies is in the Fürstenberg Archives, Donaueschingen, which has them all but No. 100. Some of these parts are on English paper and were evidently used in the original London performances before being taken back to Vienna by Haydn. The Esterházy Archives in Budapest have Elßler parts of Nos. 95, 96, 97, 99, 100,

Nr. 102 Autograph:
Staatsbibliothek zu Berlin – Preußischer Kulturbesitz, Musikabteilung
Abschrift:
Salomons Londoner Abschrift; wie Nr. 93

Nr. 103 Autograph:
British Library London (drei Seiten des Menuetts in fremder Handschrift)
Abschrift:
Salomons Londoner Abschrift; wie Nr. 93

Nr. 104 Autograph:
Staatsbibliothek zu Berlin – Preußischer Kulturbesitz, Musikabteilung
Abschrift:
Salomons Londoner Abschrift; wie Nr. 93

Mit Ausnahme von Nr. 93 und dem fehlenden langsamen Satz von Nr. 100 sind also die autographen Partituren der Londoner Sinfonien nahezu unversehrt erhalten. Die Abschriften, die in London für Salomon angefertigt worden waren, wurden vor einigen Jahren (1982) von Alec Hyatt King entdeckt; sie sind außerordentlich wichtig.

II. Handschriftliches Orchestermaterial von Johann Elßler

Orchesterstimmen, die nach den autographen Partituren von Haydns eigenem Kopisten geschrieben wurden, viele mit Korrekturen in der Handschrift des Komponisten, sind selbstverständlich von großem Wert bei der Ermittlung eines zuverlässigen Notentextes für die Londoner Sinfonien. Die umfassendste Sammlung ist im Besitz des Fürstenbergischen Archivs in Donaueschingen, wo alle Londoner Sinfonien außer Nr. 100 vorhanden sind. Einige dieser Stimmen sind auf Papier englischer Herkunft geschrieben und offenbar bei den Londoner Aufführungen benutzt worden,

101 and 103 (the latter lacking the Minuet), and the Öttingen-Wallerstein Archives in Harburg have Nos. 93, 96, 97 and 98.

III. London manuscript scores

In 1795 and 1796 respectively, Haydn presented Salomon with the exclusive rights to both sets of London symphonies, a very proper gesture to the man who had commissioned them and had led the orchestra for the first performances of nine of them (the last three symphonies were presented by the newly-formed 'Opera Concert' at the King's Theatre under the direction of Giovanni Battista Viotti). The tangible aspect of this handsome gift was a complete set of scores – the autographs of Nos. 95 and 96 and copies of the rest, as set out in I above. In November 1791, Haydn sent copy scores of Nos. 95 and 96 to his friend in Vienna, Bernhard von Kees. They evidently arrived safely since von Kees entered the opening bars of both works in his catalogue of Haydn symphonies with the words 'NB von London gekommen', but these scores have not been located.

IV. Printed orchestral material by Robert Birchall, London

There can be no doubt that Salomon also had his own personal set of orchestral parts of all 12 symphonies. He had them engraved, after Haydn's return to Vienna (as the terms of the presentation entitled him to do), with at least one publisher (Monzani & Cimador) and he may also have sold them to others. A year or two after Haydn's death (1809) Salomon entered into an agreement with Robert Birchall (who had earlier published Salomon's arrangements for Piano

bevor Haydn sie mit zurück nach Wien nahm. Das Esterházy-Archiv in Budapest besitzt Stimmen von Elßler zu Nr. 95, 96, 97, 99, 100, 101 und 103 (diese ohne Menuett), und das Archiv Öttingen-Wallerstein in Harburg Nr. 93, 96, 97 und 98.

III. Londoner handschriftliche Partituren

1795 bzw. 1796 übertrug Haydn die Exklusivrechte beider Folgen der Londoner Sinfonien an Salomon – eine noble Geste dem Mann gegenüber, der sie in Auftrag gegeben hatte und unter dessen Leitung als Konzertmeister neun von ihnen uraufgeführt worden waren (die letzten drei Sinfonien wurden im King's Theatre vom neu gegründeten „Opera Concert" unter der Leitung von Giovanni Battista Viotti aufgeführt.) Der „materielle Aspekt" dieses noblen Geschenks bestand aus einem vollständigen Satz Partituren – den Autographen von Nr. 95 und 96 und Kopien der restlichen Werke, wie in Abschnitt I ausgeführt. Im November 1791 schickte Haydn Abschriften der Partituren von Nr. 95 und 96 an seinen Wiener Freund Bernhard von Kees. Offenbar sind sie wohlbehalten angekommen, denn von Kees setzte zu den Anfangstakten beider Werke in seinem Verzeichnis der Sinfonien Haydns den Vermerk hinzu: „NB von London gekommen". Die Partituren selbst wurden allerdings bisher nicht aufgefunden.

IV. Gedrucktes Orchestermaterial von Robert Birchall, London

Zweifellos besaß auch Salomon von allen zwölf Sinfonien seinen eigenen Satz Orchesterstimmen. Nach Haydns Rückkehr nach Wien ließ er sie (wozu er nach den Bedingungen der Übereignung berechtigt war) von wenigstens einem Verleger stechen (Monzani & Cimador), und möglicherweise hat er sie außerdem an weitere verkauft. Ein oder zwei Jahre nach Haydns Tod (1809) schloß Salomon eine Vereinbarung mit Robert Birchall (der schon zuvor Salo-

Trio and for Flute and String Quartet with optional Piano of the London symphonies) for a new issue of the orchestral parts. If Landon is right in supposing that Salomon provided Birchall with his own performing material for this print – possibly the very material he had used under Haydn's direction – it would explain not only the high intelligence and practical nature of the editings, but, more important, the often close relationship between Birchall and the autographs, and the even closer relationship between Birchall and the copy scores that Haydn presented to Salomon.

The Birchall print thus has a high place among the sources upon which this edition is based. With so strong a link – Salomon – between it and Haydn and its readiness as a performing edition, it has a combination of virtues that will be of interest to both scholars and performers. Where the Birchall differs from our other sources (generally because of changes that Haydn made after his return to Vienna that would have been unknown to Salomon) such variants, as well as others of interest, are shown in the Textual Notes below.

Editorial method

Redundant cautionary or parallel accidentals have in some cases been omitted. Haydn's habit of reminding players constantly of such accidentals in continuously modulating passages, even if it means repeating them in the same bar, makes it difficult to follow this aim with complete consistency, and in such cases we have omitted only those which, in modern practice, might confuse rather than clarify.

mons Bearbeitungen der Londoner Sinfonien für Klaviertrio sowie für Flöte und Streichquartett und Klavier ad libitum veröffentlicht hatte) über eine Neuausgabe der Orchesterstimmen. Falls Landon mit seiner Annahme recht hat, daß Salomon für diesen Druck Birchall sein eigenes Orchestermaterial zur Verfügung stellte – möglicherweise dasselbe Material, das er bereits unter Haydns Leitung benutzt hatte –, würde dies nicht nur den hohen Standard und den praktischen Charakter der Ausgaben erklären, sondern darüber hinaus auch die oft enge Beziehung zwischen den Stimmen von Birchall und den Autographen und – mit sogar noch größerer Übereinstimmung – zwischen dem Birchall-Druck und den Partitur-Abschriften, die Haydn Salomon geschenkt hatte.

Der Birchall-Druck besitzt also unter den Quellen, auf denen die vorliegende Edition basiert, einen hohen Stellenwert. Mit seiner so engen Beziehung – in der Person Salomons – zu Haydn selbst und mit seiner Tauglichkeit als Aufführungsmaterial verbindet er Vorzüge miteinander, die sowohl für Wissenschaftler wie auch ausübende Musiker von Interesse sind. Wo Birchall von unseren übrigen Quellen abweicht (die Ursache besteht hauptsächlich in Änderungen, die Haydn nach seiner Rückkehr nach Wien vornahm und die Salomon deshalb unbekannt bleiben mußten), werden die Varianten neben anderen wesentlichen Lesarten in den Einzelanmerkungen unten ausgewiesen.

Editionsprinzipien

Überflüssige Warnungs- oder wiederholte Akzidentien wurden in einigen Fällen gestrichen. Haydns Gewohnheit, in kontinuierlich modulierenden Passagen den Spielern solche Akzidentien zur Erinnerung fortwährend vorzuschreiben, selbst wenn sie dadurch im selben Takt wiederholt werden, erschwert es, dieses Prinzip konsequent durchzuhalten. In solchen Fällen wurden nur diejenigen Zeichen getilgt, die nach

Missing accidentals, staccato signs, slurs, ties and dynamics etc., have been added without comment only where their absence is the obvious result of the composer's, copyist's or engraver's oversight. Where explanatory comment may be helpful this will be found in the Textual Notes below.

Square brackets and broken ties and slurs indicate editorial additions in the text. The basis for such additions (i.e. parallel or analogous passages) will be clear by the context.

We have retained the indication *Tutti* (used by Haydn to cancel a previous *Solo*, usually in the woodwind) wherever it appears in our sources. Where it is clearly implied by the context but not shown in any of the sources, we have used the modern equivalent – [a 2] where the two parts are in unison.

Since Haydn and Elßler generally wrote a staccato as a quick stroke, it is difficult to determine whether a difference in performance is intended between a stroke and a dot. In general we have used dots except where a sharply accented staccato seems required.

SYMPHONY No. 95

This symphony was composed for Haydn's first visit to London – one of the six commissioned by Johann Peter Salomon for the impresario's 1791/2 season, the first concert of which had taken place on 11 March 1791. Like the other five of the first six 'London' symphonies (Haydn was to compose another six symphonies for his second

heutigem Gebrauch den Spieler eher verwirren, als daß sie Klarheit schaffen.

Fehlende Akzidentien, Staccato-Zeichen, Artikulations- und Bindebögen, dynamische Bezeichnungen etc. wurden stillschweigend nur dann ergänzt, wenn sie offensichtlich vom Komponisten, Kopisten oder Stecher übersehen wurden. Wenn eine Erläuterung angebracht erscheint, ist sie unten in den Einzelanmerkungen zu finden.

Mit eckigen Klammern und als gestrichelte Bögen sind Herausgeberzusätze im Notentext gekennzeichnet. Die Begründung für solche Ergänzungen (parallele oder analoge Lesarten) ergibt sich aus dem Kontext.

Die Bezeichnung *Tutti*, die Haydn gewöhnlich in den Holzbläserstimmen verwendete, um ein voraufgegangenes *Solo* aufzuheben, wurde beibehalten, wo es in den benutzten Quellen erscheint. An Stellen, an denen eine Bezeichnung nach dem Kontext eindeutig erforderlich, in den Quellen jedoch nicht ersichtlich ist, wurde das heute übliche [a 2] gesetzt, wenn zwei Stimmen *unisono* spielen.

Da Haydn und Elßler die Staccato-Vorschrift in aller Regel als flüchtig dahingeworfenen Strich notierten, ist die Entscheidung schwierig, ob Strich und Punkt unterschiedlich ausgeführt werden sollen. Der Herausgeber hat grundsätzlich Punkte gesetzt, es sei denn, ein scharf akzentuiertes *staccato* schien gefordert.

SINFONIE Nr. 95

Diese Sinfonie wurde für Haydns ersten Londonaufenthalt komponiert – eine von sechs vom Impresario Johann Peter Salomon für die Konzertsaison 1791/2 bestellten Auftragskompositionen. Das erste dieser Konzerte fand am 11 März 1791 statt, und die Sinfonie Nr. 95 wurde vermutlich im April oder Mai 1791 (das genaue Datum ist

London visit in 1794/5), No. 95 was first performed in the Hanover Square Rooms probably in April or May of 1791 (the exact date has never been determined) and possibly repeated later in the season. Adhering to the practice established for these concerts, Salomon led the orchestra from the concertmaster's desk with Haydn at the keyboard. It is the only one of the 'London' symphonies in a minor key and without a slow introduction, although the slow introductions to the Symphonies 98, 101 and 104 are in the minor.

The autograph score (12-stave horizontal format) has 'Sinfonia' on the cover in Haydn's hand and at the top of the first page of music the composer's customary 'In Nomine Domine' and further to the right 'di me giuseppe Haydn London 791'. At the end of the score Haydn wrote 'Laus Deo'.

Sources

Autograph score in the British Library, London . . . . AUT
Manuscript material by Johann Elßler in the Esterházy Archives, Budapest . . . BUD
Manuscript material by Elßler in the Fürstenberg Archives, Donaueschingen . . . D/E
Printed parts by Birchall . . . . . . BIR
Birchall edition of Salomon's Quintet arrangement SAL5

Harry Newstone

Textual Notes

MS = Manuscript
Str. = Strings
Ww. = Woodwind
a/h = another hand
b(b) = bar(s)
n(n) = note(s)

The AUT seems to have been written in great haste and many of Haydn's abbreviations and/or shorthand omissions have led to textual uncertainties in the orchestral material – e.g. whether a blank bassoon stave might mean 'col basso' or not; or where flute or oboe parts are marked 'col Vln.' only to be followed by a blank stave after a page turn. Of particular interest are changes in the bassoon parts where Fg. 2 is occasionally used to strengthen the Vla. and/or Vc/Cb. line. These do not appear either in AUT, D/E or BUD but are in BIR and other printed editions which appeared between 1795 and 1805 (Haydn finally left London on 15 August 1795). Whether these changes were in the engraver's copy that Salomon provided to Birchall (i.e., his own set of MS parts) cannot now be established since these parts have either not survived or have not, so far, been found, but the fact that they are printed in BIR lends them a certain authenticity which cannot be ignored. We have in our main text shown the bassoon parts as they appear in AUT (and D/E, BUD) listing the changes as they appear in BIR in the textual notes below. Unfortunately, the Fg. 1 part is lacking in BUD.

Mov. I

D/E, BUD, BIR do not have the 'moderato', D/E, BUD have C, BIR ¢ (as AUT)

bar 1 Str. *ff* in AUT (nothing Vla.), other sources a mixture of *ff* and *f*, Vla. *ff* from D/E, BUD; BIR Str. *f*

   3 Vl. I BUD no *dolce*; BIR this figure slurred, also in bb75, 119

4, 5 (also bb76, 77, 120, 121) Vl. I all sources nn1–2 slur, editorial slur to n3 possible on basis of lower Str.; D/E, BUD, BIR nn4–6 ♩♩.♩ ditto bb120, 121 BIR which, however, has ♩♩.♩ in bb76, 77 (bb75–77, 120, 121 AUT, D/E, BUD no phrasing)

6, 7 Fg. 1, 2 slur from BIR, ditto slurs bb76–79 (where D/E, BUD b78 lack the Vl. II, Vla. slurs) and bb122–123 where BIR Vla. slur also crosses barline

8, 9 Vl. I/II editorial slurs on basis of Vla. *legato* phrasing, ditto bb15, 16 Vl. I (cf. Vl. II) and bb124–128

  15 Vl. II, Vla. n1 stacc. in AUT only; Vl. II BUD, BIR nn1–4 slur

  16 Cor. 1, 2 AUT no dynamic, Tr. no dynamic any source; Fl., Fg. nn2, 3 stacc. from BIR; Ob. 2, Cor. 1, 2 nn1–3 slur from BIR (Ob. 1 only nn1–2 slur, adjusted as Ob. 2)

	17	Cor. 2 D/E, BUD n2 as Cor. 1; Fl., Fg. , Vc/Cb. n3, b18 staccs. from BIR, ditto bb19, 20
17–20		Vl. I/II, Fl. b20 slurs from BIR
	21	Cor. 1, 2 *f* from AUT, D/E; BUD, BIR Cor. 1 *fz*, Cor. 2 *f*
20–25		Cor. 1, 2 BIR no ties
	27	Fl., Vl. I, Vla. D/E, BUD nn10–13 no slur; Vl. I BIR nn7–9 no slur but in Fl. It is difficult to tell whether the 3 ⌢ is a phrasing or just part of the triplet indication; see also bb55, 107, 109, etc.
	28	Stacc. n1 in AUT Vl. I/II only, we apply to all parts
29–35		Fg. stave blank in AUT but 'col Basso' in D/E, BUD, BIR
	36	Fg. 1, and b37 nn1–5, D/E, BUD, BIR also written for Fg. 2 (AUT does not specify whether these notes are for Fg. 1 only; ditto b38 last note to b39 nn1–5)
	38	Vl. I *pp* in AUT, BIR; D/E, BUD *p*; Fl. *p* only in BIR
41, 42		Fl., Vl. I D/E, BUD, Fg. 1 (solo) D/E only semiquavers slurred, ditto bb142, 143 Ob. 1
	43	Cor. 1, 2 n2 *f* from BIR
	44	Fg. *Tutti* from AUT but no dynamic; BIR has *f* and *a due*
45–46		Fl., Ob. 1, 2 slur across barline from BIR, ditto bb50–52 Ww, Cor. 1, 2
	51	Vl. II D/E, BUD nn10–12 lacking b♭
	54	Vla. BIR grace note e♭ and *ff* for Ob. 2, Fg., Vl. II, Vla., Vc/Cb. (Fl. *f*) and stacc. crotchets same parts
	57	Ob. 1 BIR n1 g♮″ (possible)
	59	Vla. n1 as D/E, BUD, BIR; AUT lacking b♭, upper note(s) unclear
	66	Vl. II, Vla., Vc/Cb. nn1–2 slur from SAL5 Vla., other sources no markings except BIR stacc.; Cor. 1, 2, Tr. 1, 2, Timp. *f*, and b67 Fg. *fz* from BIR
	69	Fl., Ob. 2 n2 *fz* (*sf*) from BIR; ditto b70 Fl., Ob. 2, Vla., Vc/Cb., b71 Fl., Ob. 2, Vla.
	70	Ob. 1 n2 *fz* all sources except AUT where it is on n3
	71	Fl., Ob. 1, Fg. 1, 2 *fz* from BIR
	72	Vl. II AUT dot after minim looks like crotchet f′ and so copied into D/E, BUD; BIR [music example]; Fg. *ff* from BIR
73, 74		General staccs. by analogy with AUT Vc/Cb. b73, Vla. b74; BIR has stacc. dots or strokes on all crotchets bb72–74

80	Vla. nn1, 3 stacc. only in AUT
80–83	Stacc. crotchets from BIR, partly supported in D/E, BUD
84	Fg. 1 D/E e♭′
85–86	Cor. 1, 2 BIR no tie
86	Fg. 2 D/E, BUD g
87	Fl., Ob. 2 AUT staves blank after page turn, Fl., D/E, BUD bar rest, BIR [music example], ditto Ob. 2 D/E, BUD, BIR but lacking ♮ in D/E, BUD; Cor. 1, 2 AUT originally [music example] which is still in D/E, BUD with the *p*; BIR follows AUT correction as in our text with *p* here for Cor. 1 and in b88 for Cor. 2; b89 Fl. *p* from BIR
87–88	Fg., Vla. nn1–8 slur from BIR, which has Fg. 2 octave below Fg. 1
89–91	Vla. from D/E, BUD, BIR; AUT stave blank
91–93	Cor. 1 AUT no ties
93	Vl. I AUT n5 looks like d″ changed to f″, D/E, BUD d″, BIR, SAL5 f″ which we think is correct; D/E, BUD have the *f* in the next bar, BIR under the barline
94	Vl. I n4 D/E, BUD, BIR crotchet, ditto Fl D/E, BUD because AUT looks like crotchet and lacks first quaver rest; Cor 1, 2 *f* from BIR; bb94, 95, 97 Fl., and b95 Vl. I BIR slur nn1–4; b96 Fl. BIR slur on semiquavers
95	Fg. 2 BIR [music example]
100–102	Fg. stave AUT blank, other sources Fg. as Vc/Cb.
103	Fg. 2 BIR [music example]; Vl. I/II nn7–9 AUT [music example] (middle note a little low), D/E Vl. I [music example], Vl. II originally [music example] altered (a/h) to [music example], BUD Vl. I/II [music example], BIR Vl. I/II, SAL5 Vl. I as AUT. We follow D/E alteration (presumably made upon Haydn's instruction) although AUT, BIR, SAL5 version equally possible.
104	General *ff* and stacc. crotchets in bb104, 105, b106 nn1, 2 from BIR; Ob. 2 b104 nn1–2 slur from BIR
108, 109	Vl. II, Vla. slurs by analogy with Ob. 1, 2 (BIR crotchets stacc.)
113	Vla. *fz* from BUD; D/E *for.*, BIR *f*, AUT nothing
113–115	Fg. AUT still in bass clef, ditto D/E, BUD but b113 n3 e♭′; BIR Fg. 1 as AUT but correctly in tenor clef and Fg. 2 [music example]; all stacc. crotchets from BIR

XVIII

116   Ob. 1 *Solo* and *p* from BIR, ditto Ob. 2 b117 where D/E Ob. 1 marked *Solo*

119   Vl. I *p* from D/E (a/h), BIR; *dolce* by analogy with b3

129   Vl. I D/E, BUD, BIR n2 stacc., ditto D/E, BUD b130 n3; b129 Vl. I *dol* before n2 in BIR (D/E *p* here in a/h)

130   Ob. 1 *dol*. in BIR where both Obs. marked *Solo*, as D/E Ob. 1

133   Fg. 2 BIR n6 g

137–143   Ob. 1 D/E marked *Solo* but these bars also written into Ob. 2, ditto BUD, BIR

139, 141   Vl. *Solo* not in D/E, BUD (perhaps added later in AUT), stacc. for Solo from SAL5 and b141 BIR

141, 143   Ob. 1 last note quaver in AUT and so in other sources (except SAL5 Fl.), probably Haydn's shorthand in this context for semiquaver; b143 Ob. 2 BIR last note quaver f' under Ob. 1 a' (see 137–143 above)

144   Vl. II D/E, BUD n2 *fz*; Vc/Cb. D/E, BUD, BIR n2 *f*

145   Ob. 1, Fg. *f* from BIR

146   Vl. I n1 stacc. only in AUT

147–148   Fl. tie possible (?AUT), tie to b149 from BIR; b148 Cor. 1, 2, Tr. 1, 2, Timp. D/E, BUD *f*, BIR *ff* (as AUT)

148   Timp. all sources ♩ ♫ ♩ ♩ , our dotted rhythm on basis of Cor., Tr., the same possible for Timp. in b150

151   Fl., Ob. 2, Vl. II, Vc/Cb. BIR *ff*, ditto b153 Vla. and b155 Ob. 1 (Ob. 2 *fz* as AUT), Fg. Cor. 1, 2; bb151–153, 155–158 all crotchet staccs. from BIR

157   Vla. nn3–5 AUT, BIR, SAL5 c', our a from D/E, BUD (possibly a later change by Haydn on basis of Vl. I)

161   Tr. 1, 2 , Timp. BIR *ff* (SAL5 Vla. which has Cor. parts here has the additional *ff*)

Mov. II

AUT, BIR (not Vl. I/II), SAL5 *Andante* only, *Andante cantabile* from D/E, BUD, BIR (Vl. I/II). In this movement there is very little phrasing in AUT, D/E, BUD, but BIR, whose readings we have for the most part accepted (detailed below), is more comprehensively phrased.

1   Vl. I AUT n3 grace note (appoggiatura?) unclear but written ♪, in other sources ♪. In performance this would be played ♪ (as an appoggiatura) as we show it; Vl. I nn5, 6 staccs. from AUT, D/E, BUD (this time only, later no phrasing) in BIR, SAL5 this group printed ♪♫ , ditto bb31, 47 (slur lacking in SAL5), 61.

2 Vl. I grace notes ♫ as AUT (ditto middle of b3 and later), other sources ♫ throughout; quavers 1–3 slur from BIR, SAL5, ditto BIR bb4, 48, 50, 62, 64

3 Vla. slur (nn1–2) only in BIR, Vc/Cb. slur as in AUT; Vc. BIR and Cb. D/E, BUD, BIR nn1–3 slur (Vc. D/E, BUD slur nn2–3); at b149 Vl. II phrasing on basis of b3, Vla., Vc/Cb. D/E, BUD no phrasing, slur nn1–2 from AUT, BIR

4 Vla., Vc/Cb. gruppetto (upbeat to b5) slur from BIR, ditto b54 Vc/Cb.

5 Vc/Cb. nn5–6 slur from BIR, ditto b55 where editorial slur added to Vla. on this basis

6 Vl. I AUT nn1–2 slur but D/E, BUD nn1–3 (as all sources b20); BIR nn1–2 slur, n3 stacc.; Vl. II AUT, D/E, BUD nn1–3 no phrasing, BIR nn2–3 slur; on basis of b20 we phrase Vl. II as Vl. I; Vla., Vc/Cb. nn1–4 phrasing from BIR

7 Vc. slur from b6 from BIR, ditto bb7–8, suggested for Vl. II, Vla.; Vl. II, Vla., Vc/Cb. (b7) gruppetto slur from BIR, ditto Vl. I nn5–8 and b8 Vl. II, Vla., Vc. nn2–5 (Cb. nn1–4), also b9 Vl. I/II last beat

8 Vl. I D/E, BUD slur on last 2 semiquavers only

9 Vla. nn2–3 slur from BIR, adopted on basis of Vc/Cb. slur nn2–3

10 Vl. I/II slur from BIR; Vla. nn1–3 slur from D/E, BUD, BIR – AUT slur reaches only to n2

11 Vc. AUT nn3–6 no phrasing, we apply that from Vl. I b1, BIR has slur here; b13 nn1–3 slur from BIR

14 Vc. nn1–2 BIR slur but not Vl. II (stacc.); all sources follow AUT in placing bass clef between nn4, 5 as shown in our score, but as this produces the same note we suggest that Haydn may have intended [music example]; SAL5 here has [music example]

15 Vl. I staccs. from D/E, BUD nn1–12 (BIR staccs. nn1–9) no doubt meant to continue for rest of bar and probably for bb16–18 where SAL5 has [music example] NB last quaver rest missing as in AUT Vl. I/II, Vla. but not BIR which, like D/E, BUD has crotchet for n10 (b18). Vla. n1 AUT, BIR, SAL5 [music example], D/E, BUD have only the b♭.

18 Vl. I/II, Vla., Cb. final quaver rest lacking in AUT; Vc. stave no rests before *Solo* entry; Vc. 'Solo' end of bar only in AUT

19 Vla. nn2, 3 BIR stacc. (pizz.), at b25 slur (arco); D/E, BUD 'col' arco' beginning of bar (error for Vl. II 'col' arco' written below the stave in AUT and so mistaken for Vla.)

21, 22, 27, 28 Vl. I nn1–3 slur from BIR, SAL5; nn16–18 slur from SAL5 b27; Vl. II, Vla., Vc. nn5–7, Cb. nn4–7 phrasing from BIR

	22	Vl. II nn16–18, b23 nn1–12 phrasing from BIR, ditto bb28, 29
23, 29		Vl. I last 3 notes slur from BIR, suggested for Vl. I ; Vc/Cb. nn2–3 slur from BIR (cf. b9)
	26	Vla., Vc/Cb. nn1–2 slur from BIR; Vc. n10 all sources (not SAL5) crotchet (quaver at b20)
	32	Vl. I nn1–2 slur from BIR, possible also for nn7–8; Vl. I/II last group slur from BIR
	33	Vla. BIR slurs 3 + 3, no slur from b32
34–43		Vl. I all slurs from BIR
36, 41		Ww., Cor. 1, 2 BIR n3 as b42
	39	Vc/Cb. D/E, BUD n1 *fp* (error) from unclear *pp* in AUT; BIR *p*
	40	Vl. I AUT, D/E, BUD nn3–4 no slur, added on basis of Vl. II slur same sources, and BIR where Vl. I nn1–4 slur
	41	AUT Ww., Cor. 1, 2 Vla. *f,* Vl. I/II Vc/Cb. *ff*; our general *ff* from BIR
	44	Vla. D/E, BUD, BIR n1 crotchet with quaver rest
	45	Vl. I from n3 to b46 n1 slurs from BIR
47–50		Fg. D/E, BUD, BIR as Vc/Cb., AUT stave blank bb43–50
	52	Cor. 1 n2 d″, Cor. 2 smudged in AUT (BIR has c″); D/E, BUD, Cor. 1, 2 n2 c″; Vl. I/II last 2 notes slur from BIR (as Ob. 2 all sources)
	54	Vl. I/II slurs from BIR, ditto Vc/Cb. slur end of bar. Cor. 2 n3 as Cor. 1 D/E, BUD; BIR has e′ as AUT
54–55		Ob. 1, 2, Fg. 1, 2, Cor. 1, 2 ⌒ across barline from BIR (NB ⌒ in Cor. 1, 2 and Fl., Ob. 1, 2, Cor. 1, 2 bb56–59, all from BIR); Vla. b55 nn1–2 slur from BIR
	56	Vla. nn1–3 AUT originally [notation] changed to [notation], D/E, BUD, SAL5 have the earlier version, BIR the later with 3-note slur which is also applied to Vc., Cb. ; Fg. 1, 2 BIR nn1–3 as Vc/Cb., Fg. 1 last note has *p* in BIR with *f* last note b58, and bb57, 58 nn2–3 slurred; Fg. 2 BIR as Vc. from b57 (marked *p*)–b60 n4
57–58		Str. phrasing from BIR, also b59 Vl. I nn1–8
	60	Vl. I nn9–10 slur, and Fl., Ob. 1, 2, Cor. 1, 2 stacc. from BIR
61–65		Fg. AUT stave blank; bb63–65 D/E, BUD, BIR (also BIR n1 b66) as Vc/Cb.
	62	Vla. nn2–3 slur from BIR
64, 65		Vl. I last group slur from BIR, ditto Fl. gruppetto bb65, 66; b64 D/E, BUD Vl. II nn1–4 [notation] ; BIR as AUT which is not very clear; b64 Vl. II demisemi-

XXI

quaver phrasing from BIR, same pattern bb65, 66, other sources nothing, which could mean legato (perhaps ♫♫♫ ♫♫♫ ♫♫♫ etc.)

66–68 Vl. I AUT demisemiquavers slurred in twos (with some missing); D/E, BUD, BIR ♫♫♫♫♫ with 4-note slur missing in D/E, BUD end of b67 and in b68; (SAL5 ♫♫♫♫♫ bb66–68)

70 Ww., Cor 1, 2, AUT *p*, *f* (except Ob. 1 *pp*, *ff*), D/E, BUD *p*, *f* (except Fl. nothing); BIR *pp*, *f* (except Fg. 1, 2 *ff*); Str. AUT *ff* (except Vla. *f*); D/E, BUD, BIR Vl. I, Vc/Cb. *ff*, Vl. II, Vla. *f*; AUT, D/E, BUD stacc. in Vc/Cb only, BIR in all parts except Ob. 1, 2, Fg. 1, 2, Vl. I/II

Mov. III

1–4 Fg. stave blank in AUT, Fg. as Vc/Cb. in D/E, BUD, BIR, ditto bb9–12, 23–26, 31–34 (in bb12, 26 AUT has 2 crotchet rests beginning of bar suggesting that the blank bars = rests); bb45–47 AUT stave blank, BIR has rests, D/E, BUD = Vc/Cb.

3 Vl. I nn3–6 ♪♪♪ on basis of AUT b11 where D/E, BUD, BIR have ♪♪♪ ; BIR b3 ♪♪♪♪ but at b33 ♪♪♪♪ , no phrasing other sources

5 (and 7, 8, 13, 15, 16, 35, 37, 38, 49, 51, 53) All quaver slurs (Fl., Ob. 1, Vl. I/II) from BIR (b16 Fl. nn1–2 slur in AUT); b5 grace note only in Fl. AUT (very small) but in b35 present in Fl., Vl. I/II all sources except BIR; b53 grace note in all sources except Fl. D/E, BUD

6, 36 Vl. II AUT, D/E, BUD slur lacking but present in BIR where (b6) Fl., Ob. 1 slur only nn1–2; b36 Fl., Ob. 1, Vl. I/II AUT, D/E, BUD, BIR Fl., no phrasing, Ob. 1, Vl. I BIR nn1–2 slur, Vl. II nn1–3 slur

7–8 Fg. 1, 2 slur from BIR, possible for Ob. 2 and in bb37–38

10 Vl. II AUT n2 originally e♭′, Vla. n2 originally g′

13 Fl. BIR slur nn3–4 only

18–21 Ob. 1 grace notes AUT, BIR clearly ♪, but D/E, BUD, BIR written ♪; Vl. I AUT not so clear, D/E, BUD ♪, BIR ♪; same discrepancies in bb22, 24 (Vl. I), 26–28 (Ob. 1, 2, Fg., Vla., Vc/Cb.)

29 Ob. 1 n1 D/E, BUD a♭″; Cor. 1, 2 Tr. 1, 2 D/E, BUD no slur to b30 (Tr. 2 D/E, BUD minim and crotchet rest); these slurs in BIR following AUT

30 Ob. 2 AUT changed from [music] to [music]; BIR has the correction and adds the slur, D/E, BUD uncorrected

35 Vla. *f* in all sources except AUT

38–42 Vla. AUT stave blank, other sources Vla. as Vc/Cb.

39–42 All parts stacc. (a mixture of dots and strokes) from BIR except Fg., Timp.,

XXII

Vla. and bb40–42 Vl. II; b39 Cor. 1 D/E, BUD *p*

46 Vl. I, Vla. slurs from BIR, possible for Vl. II (from misplaced(?) slur across barline to b47 AUT); b47 Vl. I D/E, BUD nn1–2 slur and (incorrect) *f* on n3, BIR nn1–3 slur (as AUT) but nn1–2 in Vl. II, Vla.; D/E, BUD nn2–3 slur resulting from foreshortened slur in AUT nearer end than middle of bar

48 Vl. II n2 *f* in BIR only

52–56 Vla. from D/E, BUD, BIR; AUT stave blank (after page turn)

53–54 Ob. 2 tie from BIR

55–56 Ob. 2 slur all sources, Ob. 1 from BIR

57–84 All the sources have different phrasings for Vc., AUT having the least, BIR the most. None of the MS sources is completely phrased, suggesting considerable latitude for the solo player (see b70 D/E below). Of the MS sources BUD is the most comprehensively phrased and it is this version that we show in our score with one or two editorial additions. Below we show AUT, D/E, BIR phrasings omitting those bars in which there is no phrasing at all. AUT: ♪ | ♪♪♪♪♪ |; b70 | ♪♪♪♪♪ | (slur possibly meant to cover whole bar); b72 | ♩ ♩ ♪ | D/E: ♪ | ♪♪♪♪♪ |; bb61, 62 | ♪♪♪♪♪ | ♪♪♪♪♪ | ; bb68–70 | ♪♪♪♪♪ | ♪♪♪♪♪ | ♪♪♪♪♪ | (b70 slur possibly meant to cover whole bar); for this bar a variant [music], perhaps for the repeat, has been written (a/h) on an empty stave near the bottom of the page; bb71–73 (b71 whole-bar slur?) | ♪♪♪♪♪ | ♩ ♩ ♪ | ♪♪♪♪♪ |; b76 | ♪♪♪ 𝄾 | (4-note bar slur?); bb78–82 ♩. ♪♪ | ♪♪♪♪♪ | ♪♪♪♪♪ | ♪♪♪♪♪ | (b82 whole-bar slur?), b83 | ♪♪ ♪♪♪♪ |. The phrasings in bb61, 62, 68–71, 72 (second slur), 73 (stacc.), 76, 78–82 and possibly b83 appear to have been added later (by Haydn?). BIR:

	63	Vl. II n2 D/E, BUD lower note a, our c′ from AUT, BIR, SAL5
	78	Vl. I slur in all sources except AUT
78–81,	83	Vc. phrasing from D/E, none in BUD

Mov. IV

	1–2	Vla. slur in D/E, BUD, (possible rudimentary slur in AUT), not in BIR
	3	Vla. AUT no slurs, D/E, BUD slur nn1–2 , BIR nn1–4; we add to nn3–4 by analogy with Vl. II, ditto b108
	3–4	Vc/Cb. tie in all sources except AUT, ditto bb108–109
	7	Vl. I D/E, BUD appoggiatura written ♪; nn3–6 slur on basis of b112 BIR

13, 14   Vl. II, Vla., Vc/Cb. AUT, D/E, BUD [music example] BIR avoids the parallel 5ths between Vl. II and Vc/Cb. by interchanging Vl. II, Vla. in b13 (and b118) and changing the Vla. n1 in b14 (and b119) to a, which reading we adopt

14   Vl. I AUT slur reaches only to n2, probably meant for the whole bar as shown in D/E, BUD, BIR (SAL5 as AUT)

15   Vl. I/II AUT grace note unclear, D/E, BUD, BIR, SAL5 all have ♪ for Vl. I and ♪ for Vl. II, the same at b120 except that D/E, BUD Vl. I grace note here ♪; nn3–4 slur from BIR, ditto b120

16, 121   Fg. 1, 2 *p* from BIR, ditto Fl. *p* bb17, 122

17, 19   Fl. nn1, 2 stacc. only in AUT, BIR, and Vl. I BIR; only BIR has the stacc. b21 Fl., Vl. I, ditto b122ff.

18, 20, 22–24   Fl., Vl. I AUT no quaver slurs (except b22 AUT Vl. I), all present in BIR and partly in D/E, BUD; similarly in bb28–30 Ob. 1, Vl. I where (in b28 only) the slur is in Vl. I AUT, D/E, BIR, the latter adding them in bb29, 30 and in Ob. 1; the same at bb123ff. and bb133–135 where only BIR has the slurs. At b123 Fl. D/E, BUD ♩♩♩♩ , BIR ♩♩♩♩ . (AUT not fully written out bb106–136, see below.)

22, 127   Fg. 1 D/E, BUD n4 as Fg. 2; Fg. 2 BIR n4 as in b23, ditto b127

24   Ob. 1, 2 no dynamic any source, *p* from b129 D/E, BUD, BIR

26   Vla. BIR no staccs. but present b131; Fg. staccs. (nn2–4) in AUT only

26, 27	Ob. 1, 2, Vl. I/II phrasing from AUT, the other sources have a mixture of [phrase figures] or nothing

- 28–30 Vc/Cb. slur across barline from BIR and Fg. bb28–29 AUT, ditto bb133–135

- 32ª Fg., Vla., Vc/Cb. minim in AUT, crotchet in D/E, BUD, BIR; Vl. I, Vc/Cb. BUD repeat sign only, no 1st or 2nd ending)

- 32ᵇ Fg., Vla. *f* AUT under n2, in D/E, BUD, BIR Vla. under n1, ditto Fg. BIR (no dynamic D/E, BUD); Timp. BIR *ff*; Vl. II *ff* D/E, BUD and whole bar slur BIR (ditto bb78, 80)

- 32ᵇ–36 Ob. 2 (doubling Vl. II) in AUT to page turn, then both Ob. staves blank until b44. We are inclined to believe that Haydn changed his mind about the Ob. 2 doubling (and Ob. 1 doubling Vl. I from b39?) but failed to erase these bars in AUT; D/E 2nd ending crossed out, BUD 2nd ending bar rest changed to read as 1st ending, BIR 2nd ending = 1st ending, all three sources then have rests for both Obs. until b44 which reading we adopt.

- 33, 35, 37 Fg., Vla., bb34, 36 (Vl. II), bb39, 41, 43 (Vl. I), bb78–83 (Str.), bb80–82 (Fg.), bb87–92 (Ob. 1, 2, Fg., Vl. I, Vla., Vc/Cb.) quaver slurs from BIR (b79 BIR Vl. I slur misplaced, engraved from b91 n2 to b92 n2); D/E, BUD quavers slurred only in b81 Vl. I; bb137–142 quaver slurs from BIR

- 44, 45 Cor. 1, 2 AUT stave blank, rests in other sources (Cor. 1, 2 possibly meant to double Tr. 1, 2 these bars); b45 Tr. 1, 2 D/E, BUD [figure] a misreading of the minim d″ in AUT; BIR correct ; b45 Fg. 1, 2 BIR nn3–5 slurred

- 49 Vc/Cb. AUT, D/E, BUD [figure], changed in BIR to [figure] to avoid B♭–b♮ clash with Vl. II, which alteration we adopt

- 50 Ob. 2 D/E the sharp in a/h (Haydn's?); Fg. tie to b51 from D/E Fg. 1 and BIR Fg. 1, 2; bb52–53 Ob. 2, Fg. ties from BIR

- 58 Tr. 1 D/E, BUD nn4, 5 stacc., ditto b60 BUD nn2, 3

- 59 Fg. 1 D/E d′ corrected to f♯′, Fg. 2 e♯′ uncorrected, BUD Fg. 2 (Fg. 1 lacking) e♯′ erased in favour of f♯′; Fg. 1 tie to b60 from BIR

- 61–62 Ob. 1, 2 BIR [figure]; Tr. 1 tie from BIR, added editorially to Cor. 1

- 62 Cor. 2 D/E, BUD as Cor. 1; BIR g′ (as AUT)

- 62–69 Fl. (marked 'Col Vln Imo' in AUT from b44) continues quavers in D/E, BUD but changed to crotchets in BIR, which we adopt

- 69 Vl. I D/E, BUD n8 e′, BIR, SAL5 g′ (as AUT)

- 70 Ob. 1 BUD ♭ missing; AUT Fg. 1, 2 no dynamic, Vc/Cb. *f*; BIR *fz* all parts except Fg. 1, 2, Timp. (*f*) and Tr. (nothing); b71 BIR *fz* Fl., Ob. 1, 2 Str. (Fg. 1, 2, Cor., Tr. nothing); Vla.♭ in BIR only

XXV

72 Ob. 2 BIR slur to b73

78 Fl. D/E, BUD, BIR [musical notation] followed by 8 bars rest; bb78, 79 AUT Fl. as Vla. followed by page turn and blank stave but melodic line continued in Fg., which we follow

93 Ob. 1 D/E, BUD 2 minims, BIR semibreve (as AUT)

94–95 Vla. ties from BIR

95 Vl. II AUT, SAL5 n1 have [musical notation] etc., D/E, BUD, BIR have no a′

98 Vc. D/E, BUD n3 ♯, n8 ♮ lacking, both present in separate Cb. part and in BIR; Vc/Cb. AUT (Fg.) nn7, 8 erroneously written g, f, other sources correct

98, 99 Ob. 2 AUT [musical notation] error carried into D/E. BUD, the c♯″ b99 corrected to d♯″ in BUD, our reading as in BIR

100 Cor. 2 D/E, BUD 2 minims

102 Fg., Vc. D/E, BUD n2 f (AUT e positioned too high)

106 Vl. I all sources except AUT slur only on quavers (cf. b1)

106–136 Only Vl. I written out in AUT with the instruction 'Come avanti ma senza replica'

107 Vl. I BIR no slur

111 Vl. I D/E, BUD *tr*: over n3 instead of turn

112 Vl. I nn4–6 slur from BIR

139 Vl. I n4 D/E g′ corrected (a/h) to a′, BUD g′ uncorrected, BIR, SAL5 a′ (as AUT)

144 Vl. I n6 AUT positioned a little too high, so copied as d″ into all the sources

148 Vl. I n1 AUT d′, error carried into D/E, BUD which also have a′ incorrectly for n4; BIR, SAL5 n1 e′

149 Tr. 2 D/E, BUD e′ (possibly written mechanically after previous bars), BIR c′ (as AUT)

152 Vla. AUT [musical notation], our reading from the other sources; dynamics a mixture of *ff* and *f* with some missing but mostly *ff*

154–157 Cor. 2 the stopped note b in AUT, D/E, BUD; BIR has g; some of the wind ties missing in D/E, BUD, also in bb158–163, but most are in BIR

164–165 Fl. slur and Ob. 1 tie from BIR

165–168 Fg. 2 as AUT, BIR; D/E, BUD as Fg. 1

| 168 | Vl. II AUT [music] |

| 174 | Ob. 2 BIR d″; Fg. D/E, BUD still tenor clef (AUT page turn after b169 and no bass clef b170); b175 D/E, BUD Fg. bass clef, AUT here marked 'col Basso'; BIR bass clef at b174 |

| 176 | Vl. I BIR n4 ♯ missing but space left for it |

| 177–178 | Fl., Ob. 1, 2 slur in AUT in a/h (Salomon's?), not in D/E, BUD but in BIR; b178 Vl. II second chord as in D/E, BUD, BIR; AUT, SAL5 have only the f ' |

| 181–182 | Fl. slur from BIR, possible also for Ob. 1, 2, Fg.; b181 Vl. I D/E, BUD, SAL5 grace note ♪ |

| 183 | Ww. AUT slur Ob. 2 only, D/E, BUD slur Ob. 1, 2 only, BIR Fl., Ob. 1, 2 stacc. from b182 n2 to (Ob. 2) b184 n1 |

| 185 | Vl. I slur seems to originate from b184 in AUT but in D/E, BUD over nn1–3 in b185; BIR, SAL5 nn1–4 in b185 |

| 186 | Vl. II D/E n1 c♯″ 'corrected to c♮″; Vl. II, Vla. AUT, D/E, BUD slur reaches only to n1 b187 but is probably intended for the whole bar, which is confirmed in BIR Vl. II but not Vla. which we adjust editorially; b188 Vl. II, Vla. slurs from BIR |

| 190 | Str. Vl. I/II *ff*, Vla., Vc/Cb. *f* in D/E, BUD; AUT no dynamics, BIR Vl. I *ff*, Vl. II, Vla. *f*, Vc/Cb. nothing; all winds and Timp AUT *f* except Fg. ('col Basso'), the other sources a mixture of *f* and (BIR Fl. Ob. 1, 2, Fg.) *ff* or nothing |

| 191 | Vl. I (II) BIR [music], this reading very faintly in AUT (red pencil a/h, Salomon's?) |

| 199 | General *ff* from BIR (nothing Fg. 1, 2), AUT *ff* in Vc/Cb. only (a/h?), no new dynamic D/E, BUD |

| 200 | Vl. I/II AUT [music], BUD slur only nn5–8, BIR slur only nn1–4; b202 AUT no slurs, BUD, BIR Vl. I slur only nn1–4, ditto Vl. II BIR only, b204 Vl. I/II slur nn1–4 BIR only |

| 205–211 | Fg. AUT stave blank but as Vc/Cb. in other sources; b205 last note and b206 BIR all parts except Fg., Timp., Vla., Vc/Cb. crotchets stacc. |

| 209 | Fl. all sources minim, Ob. 2 AUT minim, other sources crotchet; Vc/Cb. AUT originally minim changed (a/h?) to crotchet |

Harry Newstone

SYMPHONY No. 95

In Nomine Domini

Joseph Haydn
(1732–1809)

Edited by Harry Newstone
© 1999 Ernst Eulenburg Ltd
and Ernst Eulenburg & Co GmbH

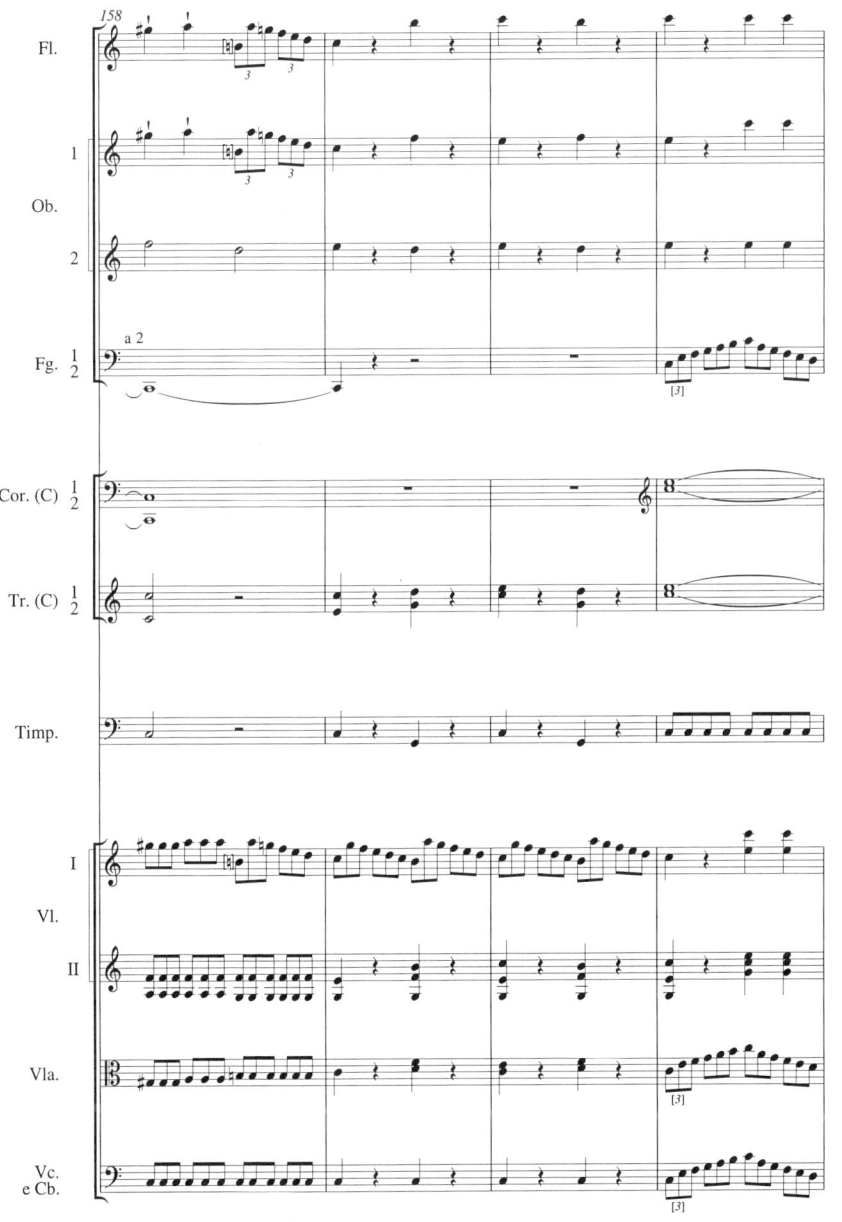

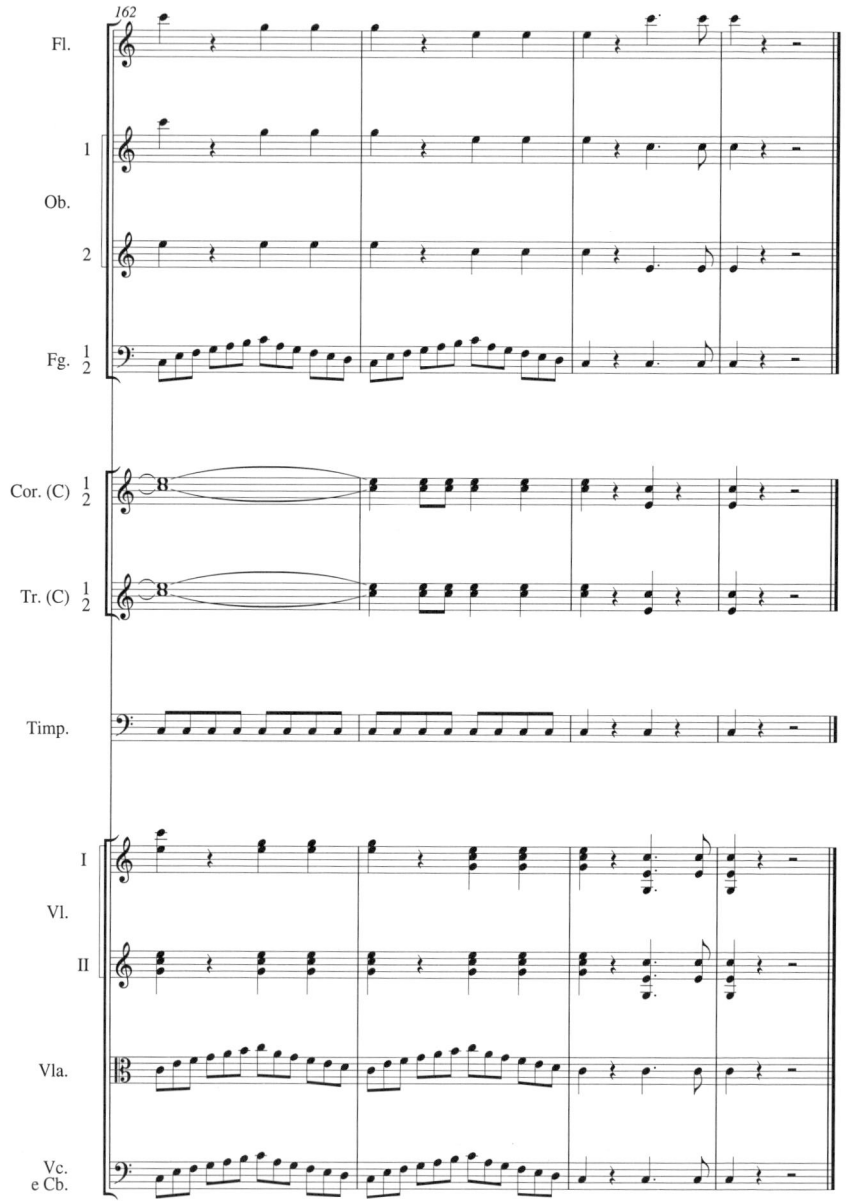

II. Andante cantabile

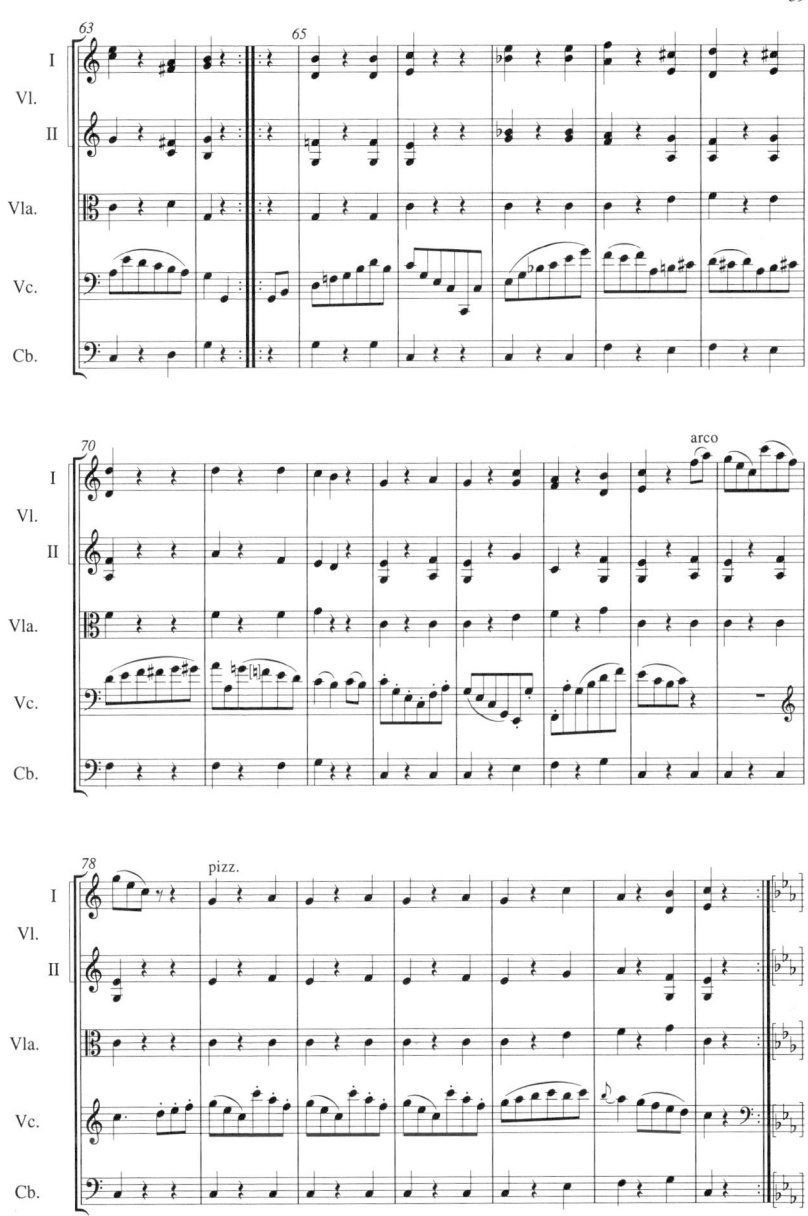

IV. Finale
Vivace

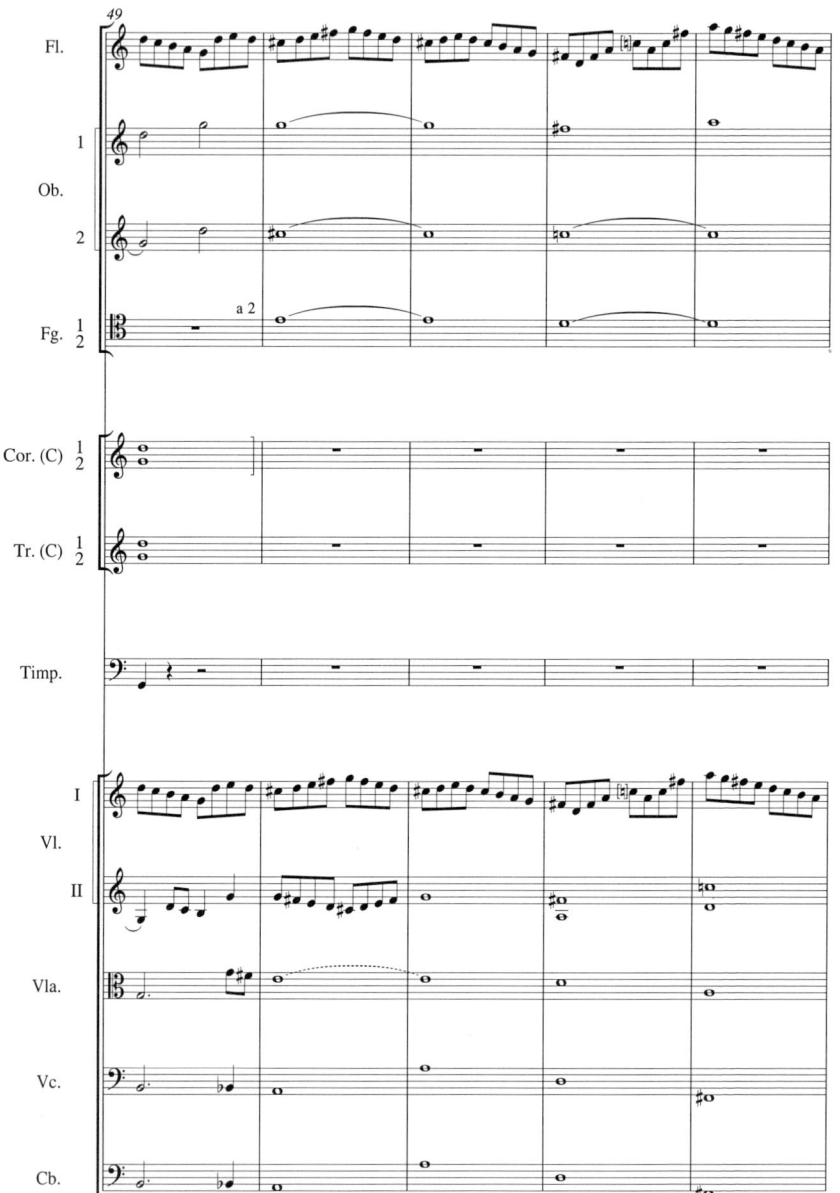

45

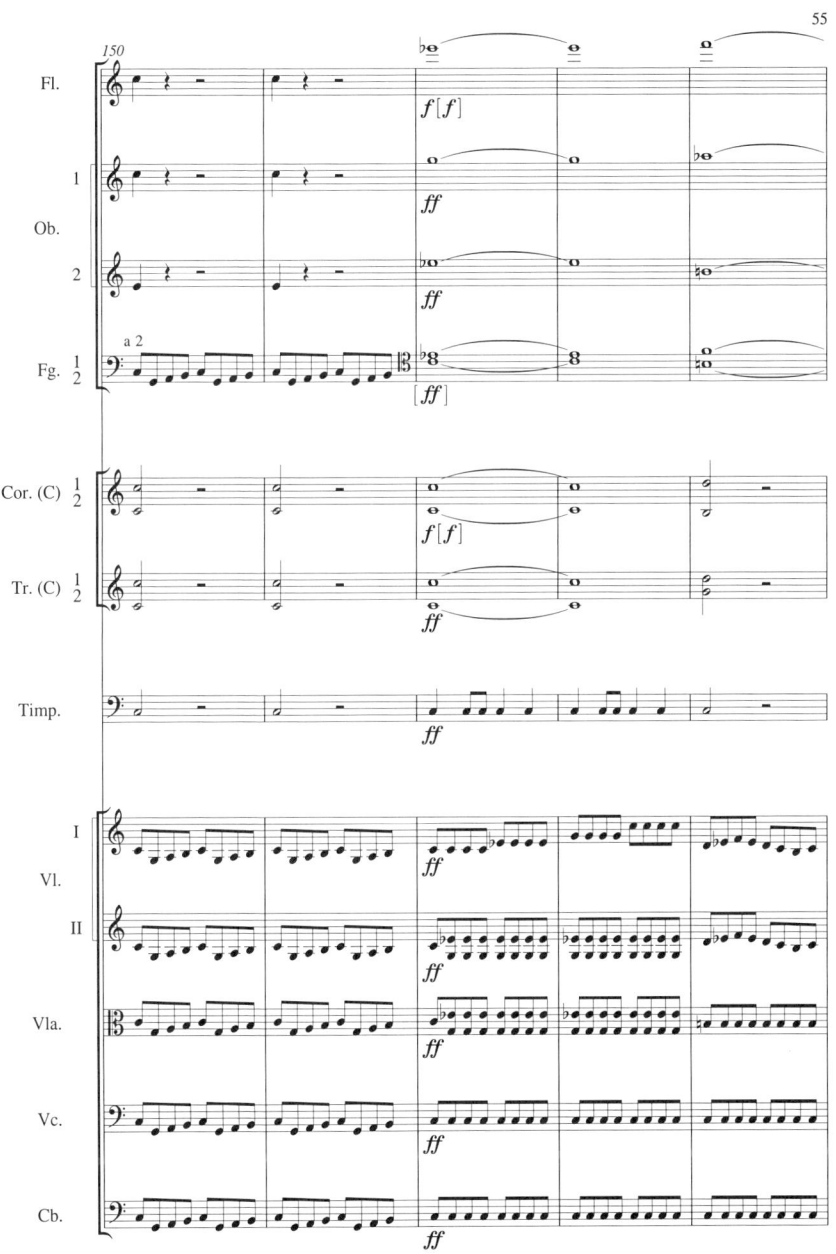

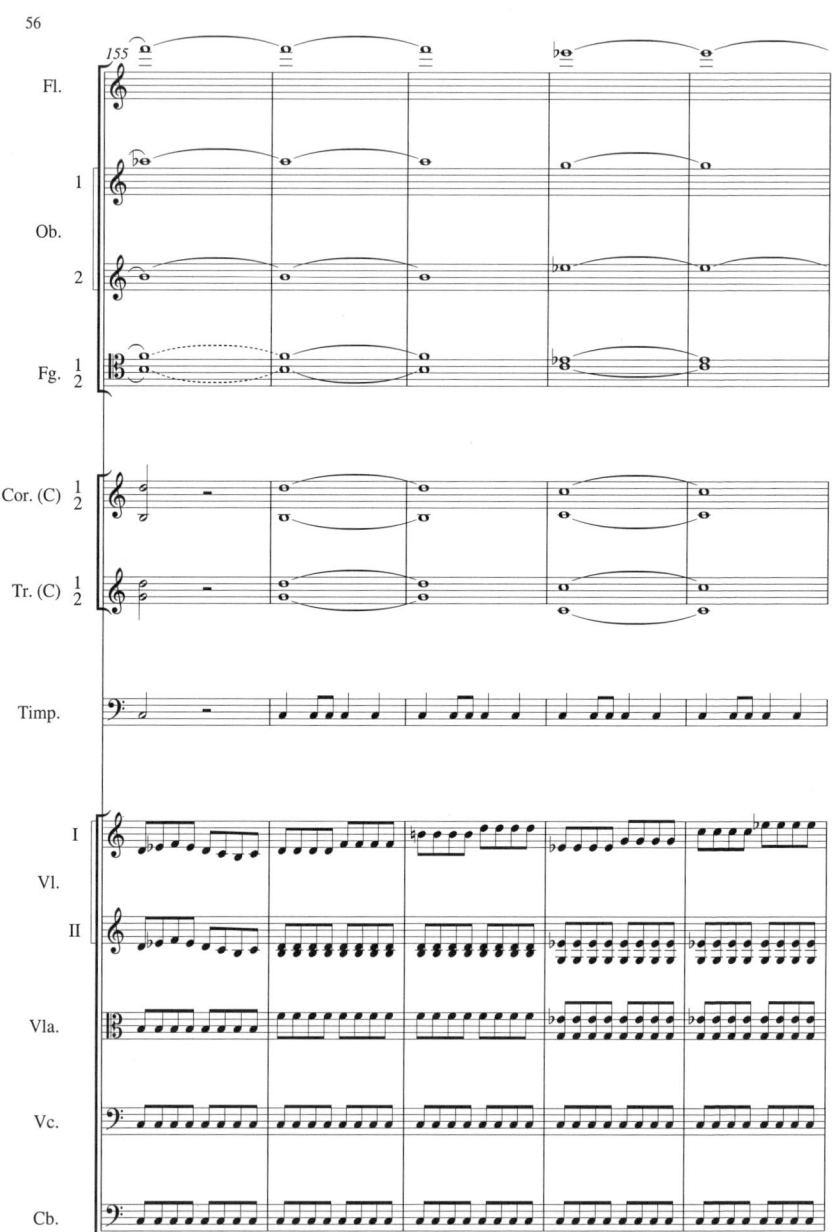

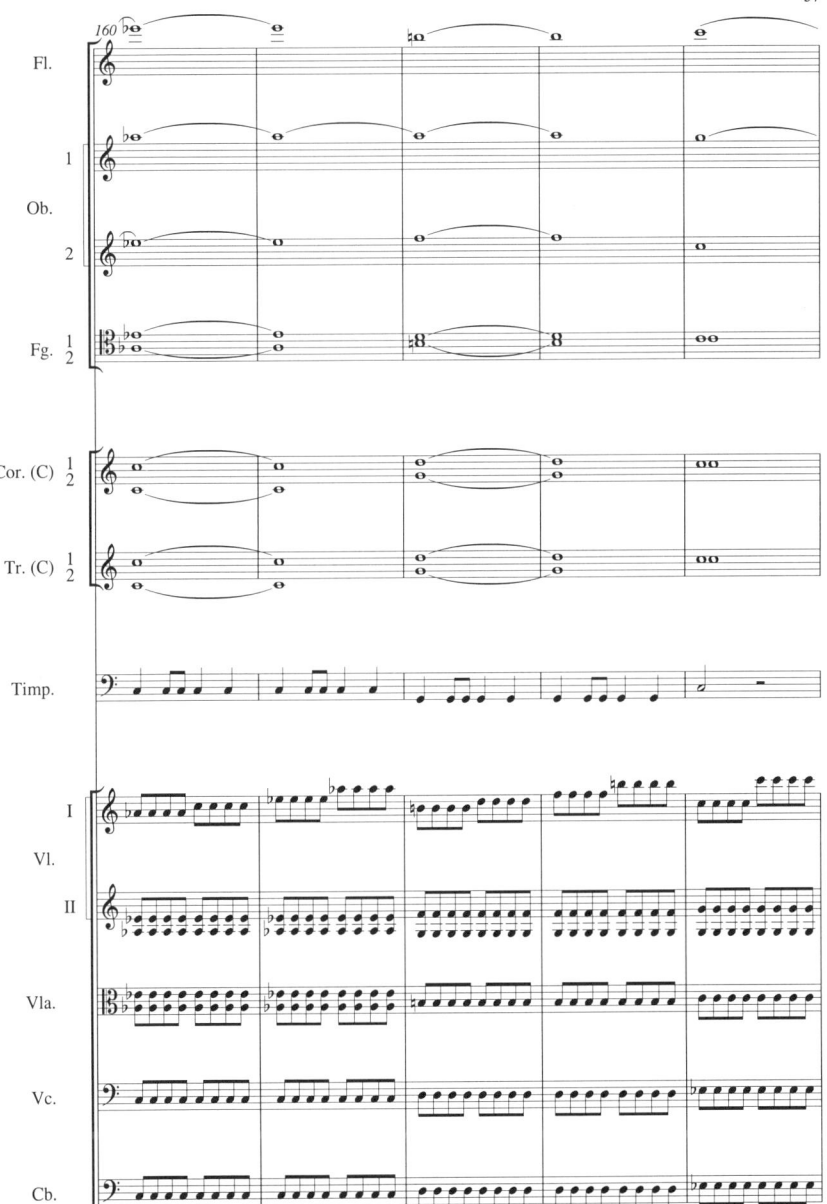

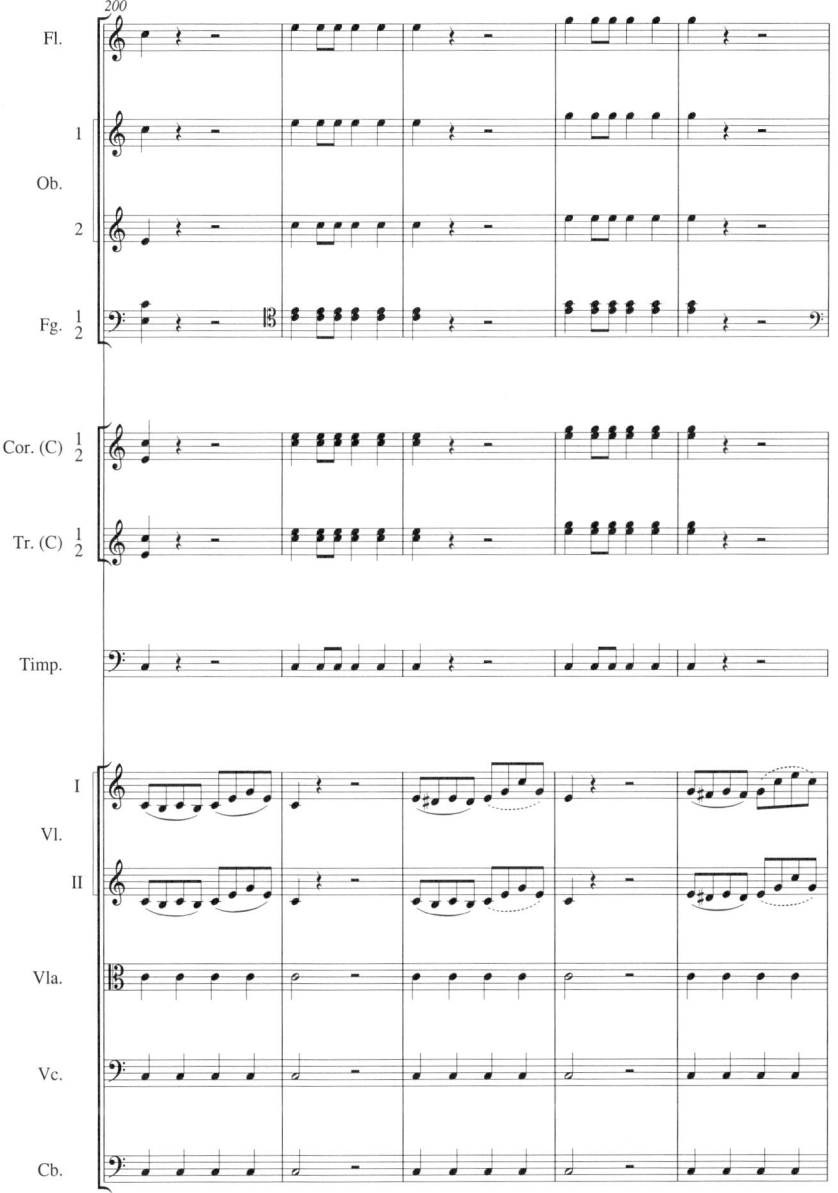

Laus Deo